# Who asked the ants?

One morning, Rabbit looked out of
her window.
"What a good day for a picnic,"
she said.
"I'll go and ask Squirrel
if he would like to go for a picnic."
And off she went to find Squirrel.

"Let's go for a picnic, Squirrel,"
said Rabbit.

"Oh yes," said Squirrel, "I'd like
that. It's a good day for a picnic.
Can Hedgehog and Badger come, too?"

Squirrel's
House

"Yes," said Rabbit.
"Tell them to come to my house."

"I'll tell them to bring lots to
eat, too," thought Squirrel.
"I always get hungry on picnics."
Then off he went to find Hedgehog.

"Would you like to come for a picnic with Rabbit and me?" he asked.

"Oh yes," said Hedgehog, "I would like that. It's a good day for a picnic."

"Good," said Squirrel.
"Come to Rabbit's house and bring lots to eat."
Then off he went to find Badger.

"Would you like to come for a picnic with Rabbit and Hedgehog and me?" he asked.

"Oh yes," said Badger, "I'd like that. It's a good day for a picnic."

"Good," said Squirrel. "Come to Rabbit's house and bring lots to eat."

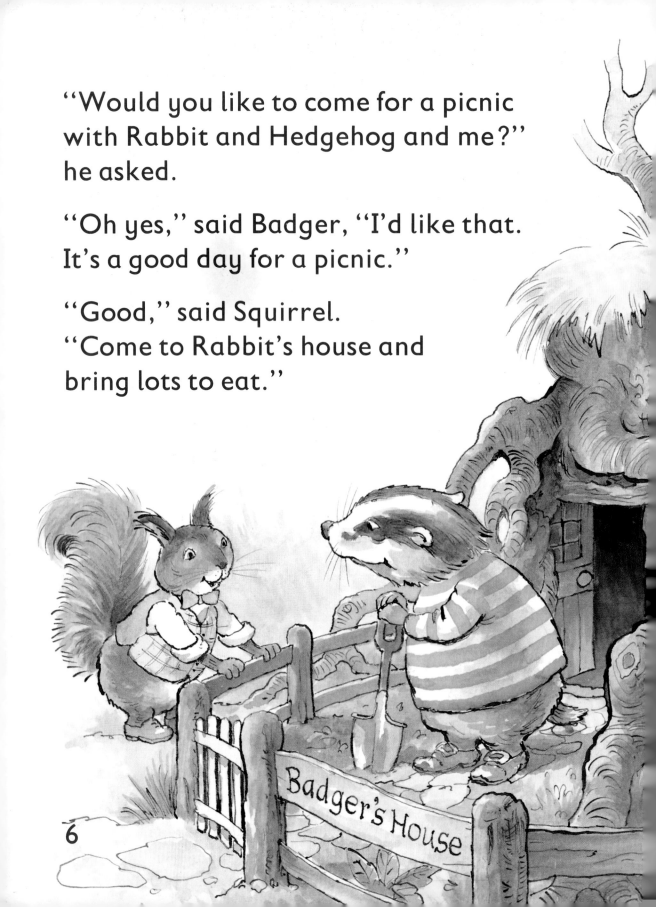

Badger's House

"I've got lots of sandwiches to eat,"
said Squirrel when they were all at
Rabbit's house.
"What did you bring, Hedgehog?"

"Chocolate biscuits," said Hedgehog.
"What did you bring, Badger?"

"Apples and crisps," said Badger.
"What have you got, Rabbit?"

"Carrot cake," said Rabbit.

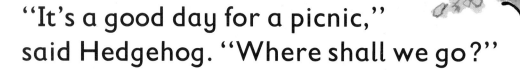

"It's a good day for a picnic,"
said Hedgehog. "Where shall we go?"

"Down to the river," said Rabbit.

"Good," said Squirrel. "I like
the river."

"So do we," said Hedgehog and
Badger.

So off they went down to the river.

"Here we are," said Rabbit.
"Let's put the picnic things under the tree.
Squirrel, put your sandwiches there.
Hedgehog, put your chocolate biscuits here. Badger, put your apples and crisps there.
And I'll put my carrot cake here."

"Now you and Badger can make the
fire," Rabbit said to Squirrel.
"And Hedgehog can go and fill
the kettle."

"It's good to have a picnic with Rabbit," said Squirrel to Badger. "She always tells us what to do."

"Yes," said Badger.

Hedgehog came back with the kettle.
"Put the kettle on the fire,
Hedgehog," said Rabbit.

"It's good to have a picnic with
Rabbit," thought Hedgehog.
"She always tells us what to do."

"Now let's paddle in the river,"
said Rabbit.

"Good," yelled Squirrel.

"Don't get wet," said Rabbit.
But Squirrel did get wet.
So did Badger.
And so did Hedgehog.

"I never get all wet when I paddle,"
said Rabbit.

14

"Is the kettle boiling, Hedgehog?"
asked Rabbit.

Hedgehog looked at the
kettle.
"Yes, it's boiling," she said.
"Let's make the tea."

"Good," said Squirrel. "I'm hungry.
Let's eat."

"Put in the tea, Hedgehog," said Rabbit.

"I have," said Hedgehog.
"It's all done."

"Look out, Hedgehog!" yelled Badger.
"The kettle is falling!"

CRASH!
Over went the kettle and out ran all the tea.

"That's it," said Rabbit.
"Now there's no tea.
That's all there was."

"But we can still eat," said
Squirrel.

17

They went to get the picnic things.
"Look," said Squirrel. "Look at
the ants! Where are all my
sandwiches?"

"Where are my chocolate biscuits?"
said Hedgehog.

"And my apples and crisps?"
said Badger.

"And where is my carrot cake?"
yelled Rabbit.

"We ate them," said the ants.
"They were good, too."

"Who asked you to come to the picnic?" said Rabbit.

"Nobody," said the ants.
"We go to all picnics.
Didn't you know?"
And off they ran.

"Cheeky things," said Rabbit.
She was cross.

"I'm hungry," said Squirrel.

"I'm hungry, too," said Badger.

"What shall we do now, Rabbit?"
asked Hedgehog.

"Let's go back to my house,"
said Rabbit. "There aren't any
ants there."

But there were!

# Did you know that.....

Wood ants go a long way
to look for food.
All the ants from one nest
use the same paths.

Each nest has its own smell.
When two ants meet, they smell
each other to see
if they are from the same nest.

Wood ants have two stomachs.
Each ant has one for its own food
and one to carry home food
to share with the other ants.

Nests can be more than one metre across
and more than thirty centimetres
above the ground and thirty centimetres
below the ground.

# Meet a real ant!

A wood ant

antenna

eye

head

leg

abdomen